PHONICS FUN

Illustrations by Marie Allen, Martha Avilés, Robin Boyer, Jane Dippold, Robert Mesheris, Christine Schneider, and George Ulrich

Photography © Art Explosion, Artville, Brand X, Dreamstime, ImageClub, Image DJ, iStock Photo, Jupiter Images Unlimited, PhotoDisc, Shutterstock, StockByte, Thinkstock
Additional photography by Siede Preis Photography and Brian Warling Photography

Customer Service: 1-800-595-8484 or customer_service@pilbooks.com

www.pilbooks.com

p i kids is a trademark of Publications International, Ltd.,
and is registered in the United States.
Brain Games is a trademark of Publications International, Ltd.

8 7 6 5 4 3 2 1

Manufactured in USA.

ISBN-10: 1-4508-3981-9
ISBN-13: 978-1-4508-3981-5

publications international, ltd.

Letter to Parents

Welcome to Brain Games!

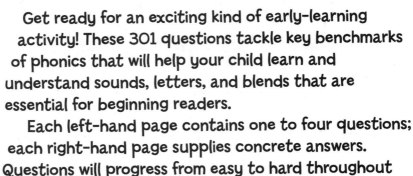

Get ready for an exciting kind of early-learning activity! These 301 questions tackle key benchmarks of phonics that will help your child learn and understand sounds, letters, and blends that are essential for beginning readers.

Each left-hand page contains one to four questions; each right-hand page supplies concrete answers. Questions will progress from easy to hard throughout the book for a graduated learning experience. Colorful illustrations and photography help to present the material in a fun and engaging way. Settle down, open the book, and have fun learning with your child today!

How to Use

- Open to the desired set of questions and answers. Fold the book in half so you and your child see only the questions.

- Read the questions aloud. Ask your child to point to, name, or complete the answer.

- Flip the book over to reveal the answers. The answers are shown in red. Miss a few? Don't worry! Every child develops a little differently—go back and try these questions again in a few days or even months. Build confidence and continue at a pace that is comfortable for your child.

Some Tips

- Your child might not be familiar with all of the content on these pages. Take the time to introduce new concepts when these kinds of questions come up.

- Encourage an older sibling or friend to share this Q&A time. Take turns asking the child questions. The older child just might learn something, too.

- Be positive and encouraging. Learning should be fun! When your child seems tired, frustrated, or unfocused, take a break. You can always play again later.

Which of these things begin with the letter **B**?

Which letter comes next? Use the picture to help.

ab___

Which letter is a vowel?

M   R

S

T   O

Trace this sight word, then practice writing it.

make

Which of these things begin with the letter **B**?

bicycle

bear

Which letter comes next? Use the picture to help.

ab <u>c</u>

Which letter is a vowel?

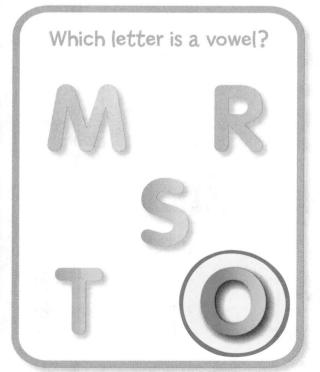

M   R

S

T   O

Trace this sight word, then practice writing it.

make

Questions

Which letter comes first? Use the picture to help.

_cd

Which letter is a vowel?

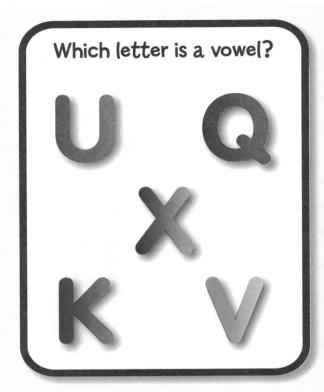

U Q
X
K V

Pair the letter **e** with the letter **r** to create an **er** sound, like in **clerk**. Help the clerk find cans that have **er** sounds.

after desert did him her apple

camera team enter hat star person

Which letter comes first? Use the picture to help.

b c d

Which letter is a vowel?

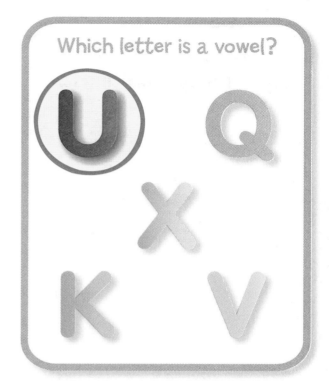

U Q X K V

Pair the letter **e** with the letter **r** to create an **er** sound, like in **clerk**. Help the clerk find cans that have **er** sounds.

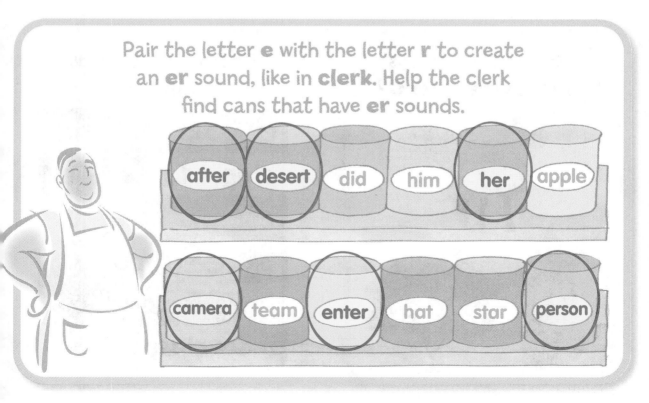

after desert did him her apple

camera team enter hat star person

Trace this sight word, then practice writing it.

What sound does the letter **B** make? Does this picture begin with the letter **B**?

Which of these things begin with the letter **C**?

Find the sight words **I** and **it**.

top	rip	for	not
stop	to	school
my	lip	van	I
bicycle	you	or
they	it	dad	cat
ax	class	bag

Trace this sight word, then practice writing it.

blue

What sound does the letter **B** make? Does this picture begin with the letter **B**?

Yes, ball begins with B.

Which of these things begin with the letter **C**?

cat

Find the sight words **I** and **it**.

top	rip	for	not
stop	to	school
my	lip	van	Ⓘ
bicycle	you	or
they	ⓘt	dad	cat
ax	class	bag

What sound does the letter **C** make? Does this picture begin with the letter **C**?

Which words in this sentence begin with the letter **B**?

This is the best book about bumblebees.

Which letter is a vowel?

W B
T
A H

Which of these things begin with the letter **D**?

What sound does the letter **C** make? Does this picture begin with the letter **C**?

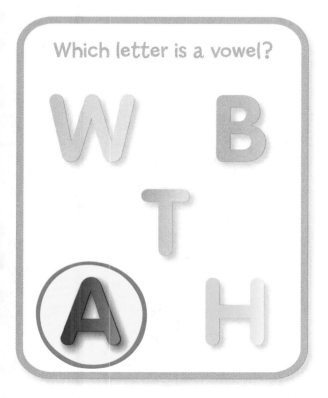

No, dog begins with D.

Which words in this sentence begin with the letter **B**?

This is the best book about bumblebees.

Which letter is a vowel?

W

B

T

A

H

Which of these things begin with the letter **D**?

dinosaur

Which of these things begin with the letter **F**?

Which letter is a vowel?

K   T

I

N   D

Trace this sight word, then practice writing it.

little

Which letter comes next? Use the picture to help.

b c ___

Which of these things begin with the letter F?

football

flag

Which letter is a vowel?

K   T

I

N   D

Trace this sight word, then practice writing it.

little

Which letter comes next? Use the picture to help.

b c <u>d</u>

Find the sight words **have** and **you**.

dark	night	am
sun	you	sun	red
on	moon	black
can	go	leg	tip
stars	a	have
day	pad	bad	for

Which of these things begin with the letter **G**?

Which letter comes next? Use the picture to help.

de___

Which words in this sentence begin with the letter **C**?

The coat in the closet has candy in its pockets.

Find the sight words **have** and **you**.

dark	night	am
sun	(you)	sun	red
on	moon	black
can	go	leg	tip
stars	a	(have)
day	pad	bad	for

Which of these things begin with the letter **G**?

giraffe

Which letter comes next? Use the picture to help.

d e **f**

Which words in this sentence begin with the letter **C**?

The **coat** in the **closet** has **candy** in its pockets.

Questions

What sound does the letter **D** make? Does this picture begin with the letter **D**?

Which letter comes next? Use the picture to help.

ef__

Which of these things begin with the letter **H**?

Trace this sight word, then practice writing it.

What sound does the letter **D** make? Does this picture begin with the letter **D**?

Yes, dress begins with D.

Which letter comes next? Use the picture to help.

e f g

Which of these things begin with the letter **H**?

heart

hippo

Trace this sight word, then practice writing it.

run

Questions

Say the word for each picture.
Which words belong in the **in** word family?

Which letter is missing from each word?
Use the pictures to help you.

__ee   __actus   __octor

Say the word for each picture.
Which words belong in the **ug** word family?

Say the word for each picture.
Which words belong in the **in** word family?

pin

chin

Which letter is missing from each word?
Use the pictures to help you.

b ee   **c** actus   **d** octor

Say the word for each picture.
Which words belong in the **ug** word family?

bug

rug

Which letter is a vowel?

What sound does the letter **F** make? Does this picture begin with the letter **F**?

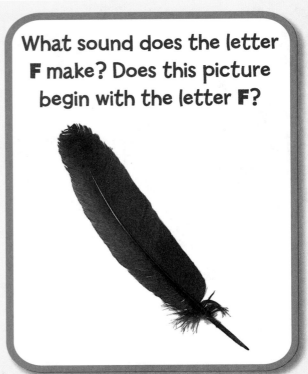

Which letter comes first? Use the picture to help.

___ i j

Which words in this sentence begin with the letter **D**?

The December school dance will be during the day.

Which letter is a vowel?

C **(E)** B J L

What sound does the letter **F** make? Does this picture begin with the letter **F**?

Yes, feather begins with F.

Which letter comes first? Use the picture to help.

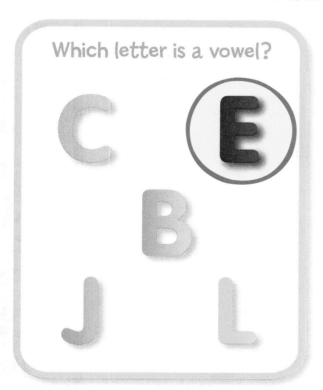

h i j

Which words in this sentence begin with the letter **D**?

The December school dance will be during the day.

Which of these things begin with the letter **J**?

Trace this sight word, then practice writing it.

look

Pair the letter **u** with the letter **r** to create a **ur** sound, like in **nurse**. Make a path from the nurse to her purse by connecting words that have a **ur** sound.

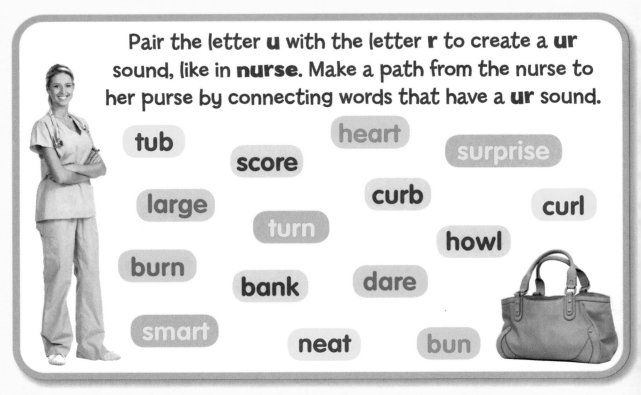

tub

heart

surprise

score

large

curb

curl

turn

howl

burn

bank

dare

smart

neat

bun

Which of these things begin with the letter J?

jar

joey

Trace this sight word, then practice writing it.

look

Pair the letter **u** with the letter **r** to create a **ur** sound, like in **nurse**. Make a path from the nurse to her purse by connecting words that have a **ur** sound.

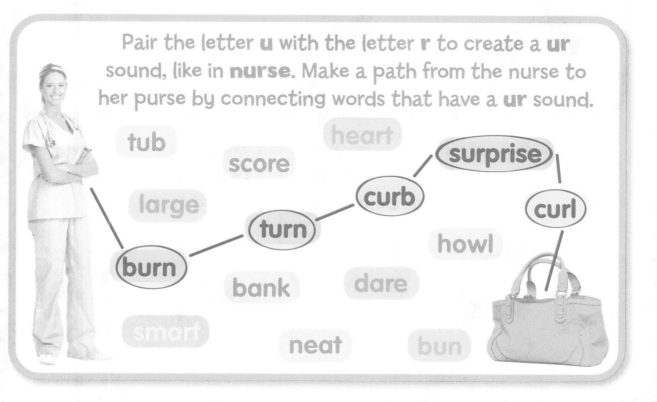

tub

heart

surprise

score

curb

large

curl

turn

burn

howl

bank

dare

smart

neat

bun

Questions

Say the word for each picture.
Which words belong in the **op** word family?

Which letter is missing from each word?
Use the pictures to help you.

__oot **__ap** **__og**

Say the word for each picture.
Which words belong in the **en** word family?

Say the word for each picture.
Which words belong in the **op** word family? **top**

mop

Which letter is missing from each word?
Use the pictures to help you.

b oot   **c** ap   **d** og

Say the word for each picture.
tent Which words belong in the **en** word family?

hen

Which of these things begin with the letter **K**?

Trace this sight word, then practice writing it.

down

When you say the word **slice**, the **s** and the **l** sounds blend together. Which words on each pizza have the **sl** sound?

sleep | slug | sun

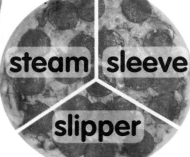

steam | sleeve | slipper

slam | sock | slime

Which of these things begin with the letter **K**?

keys

kitten

Trace this sight word, then practice writing it.

down

When you say the word **slice**, the **s** and the **l** sounds blend together. Which words on each pizza have the **sl** sound?

sleep slug sun

steam sleeve slipper

slam sock slime

What sound does the letter **G** make? Does this picture begin with the letter **G**?

Which words in this sentence begin with the letter **F**?

The family watches fireworks while they fish.

Find the sight words **three** and **look**.

one	go	off	pal
from	am	three	
is	two	so	saw
pizza	four		my
the	if	bat	out
me	mouth	look	

Which letter comes next? Use the picture to help.

hi___

What sound does the letter **G** make? Does this picture begin with the letter **G**?

Yes, goat begins with G.

Which words in this sentence begin with the letter **F**?

The **family** watches **fireworks** while they **fish**.

Find the sight words **three** and **look**.

one	go	off	pal
from	am	three	
is	two	so	saw
pizza		four	my
the	if	bat	out
me	mouth		look

Which letter comes next? Use the picture to help.

hi j

Say the word for the picture. Which sound do you hear at the beginning?

g h j

Which letter comes next? Use the picture to help.

i j ___

Which words in this sentence begin with the letter **G**?

My grandma gives the best gifts!

Find the sight words **the** and **she**.

home	sister		it
the	cat	her	for
if	mom	brother	
she	his	he	my
cousin	am		they
you	our	me	your

Say the word for the picture. Which sound do you hear at the beginning?

horse

g (h) j

Which letter comes next? Use the picture to help.

i j **k**

Which words in this sentence begin with the letter **G**?

My **grandma** **gives** the best **gifts**!

Find the sight words **the** and **she**.

home	sister		it
(the)	cat	her	for
if	mom	brother	
(she)	his	he	my
cousin	am	they	
you	our	me	your

Which letter is missing from each word?
Use the pictures to help you.

__us   __ow   __rum

Say the word for each picture.
Which words belong in the **an** word family?

Which letter is missing from each word?
Use the pictures to help you.

__ootball   __oat   __ouse

Answers

Which letter is missing from each word?
Use the pictures to help you.

_bus   **_c** ow   **_d**rum

Say the word for each picture.
Which words belong in the **an** word family?

can   **fan**

Which letter is missing from each word?
Use the pictures to help you.

_f ootball   **_g** oat   **_h** ouse

Questions

Find the sight words **he** and **up**.

them	happy	is
has	cat	top	off
up	kite	mother
dad	on	hit	sat
clock	he	pass
dog	ran	was	the

Which letter comes first? Use the picture to help.

__ m n

When you say the word **smash**, the **s** and the **m** sounds blend together. Which words below have the **sm** sound?

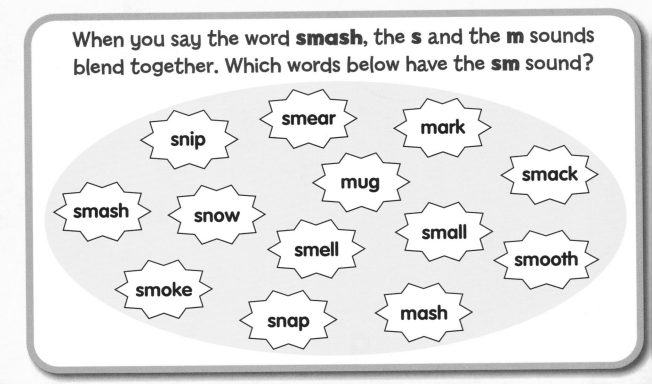

smear snip mark smack mug smash snow small smooth smell smoke snap mash

Find the sight words **he** and **up**.

them	happy	is
has	cat	top	off
(up)	kite	mother
dad	on	hit	sat
clock	(he)	pass
dog	ran	was	the

Which letter comes first? Use the picture to help.

l m n

When you say the word **smash**, the **s** and the **m** sounds blend together. Which words below have the **sm** sound?

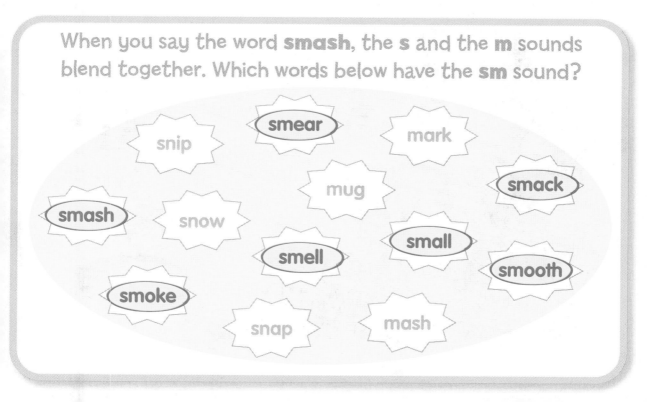

When you say the word **frog**, the **f** and the **r** sounds blend together. Help the frog cross the pond to reach the fly by drawing a path to each lily pad with the **fr** sound.

When you say the word **frog**, the **f** and the **r** sounds blend together. Help the frog cross the pond to reach the fly by drawing a path to each lily pad with the **fr** sound.

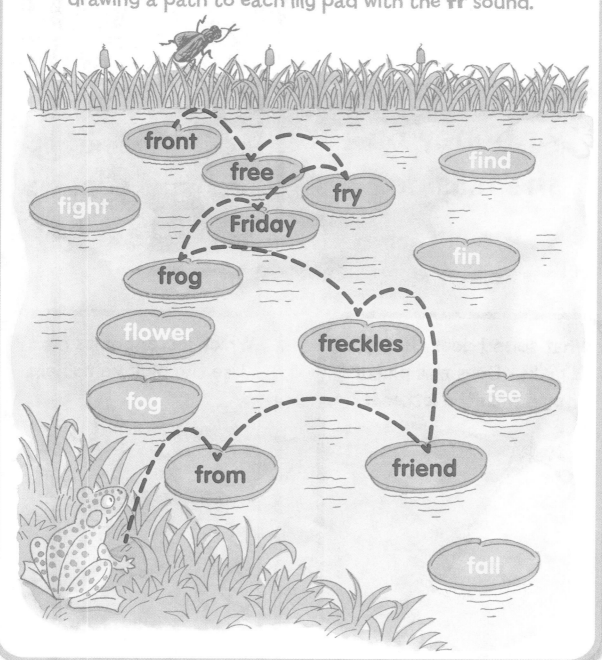

Which words in this sentence begin with the letter **H**?

He was hunting for honey on the hillside.

Find the sight words **to** and **here**.

mat	if	top	off
trap	to	Sunday	
my	pat	tip	on
sound	mine	up	
hop	sad	gap	lip
of	listen	here	

What sound does the letter **H** make? Does this picture begin with the letter **H**?

Which letter comes next? Use the picture to help.

kl___

Which words in this sentence begin with the letter **H**?

He was **hunting** for **honey** on the **hillside**.

Find the sight words **to** and **here**.

mat	if	top	off
trap	(to)	Sunday	
my	pat	tip	on
sound	mine	up	
hop	sad	gap	lip
of	listen	(here)	

What sound does the letter **H** make? Does this picture begin with the letter **H**?

Yes, hammer begins with H.

Which letter comes next? Use the picture to help.

k l m

Which letter comes next?
Use the picture to help.

Im___

Which words in this
sentence begin with
the letter **K**?

**The kettle in the
kitchen is kept
on the stove.**

Which of these things
begin with the letter **L**?

What sound does the letter
J make? Does this picture
begin with the letter **J**?

Which letter comes next? Use the picture to help.

l m **n**

Which words in this sentence begin with the letter **K**?

The **kettle** in the **kitchen** is **kept** on the stove.

Which of these things begin with the letter **L**?

log

leaf

What sound does the letter **J** make? Does this picture begin with the letter **J**?

No, watermelon begins with W.

Questions

Which letter is missing from each word?
Use the pictures to help you.

  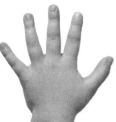

__ish   __lasses   __and

Say the word for each picture.
Which words belong in the **it** word family?

Which letter is missing from each word?
Use the pictures to help you.

__eet   __old   __orse

Which letter is missing from each word?
Use the pictures to help you.

f ish   **g** lasses   **h** and

Say the word for each picture.
Which words belong in the **it** word family?

mitten   **kitten**

Which letter is missing from each word?
Use the pictures to help you.

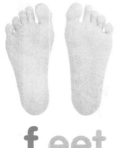  

f eet   **g** old   **h** orse

Questions

When you say the word **prince**, the **p** and the **r** sounds blend together. Help the prince find the prize by following the path of words that begin with the **pr** sound.

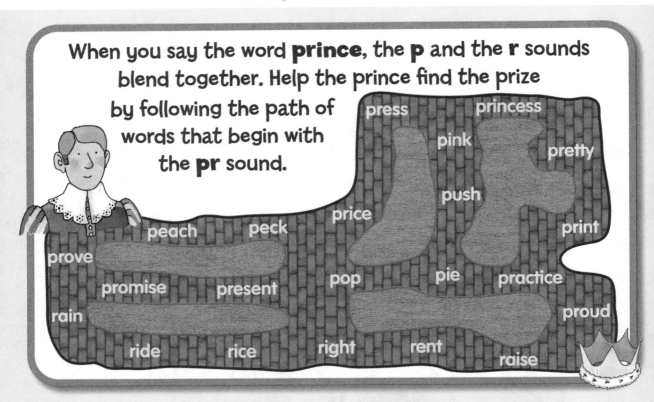

press
princess
pink
pretty
push
price
print
peach
peck
prove
promise
present
pop
pie
practice
rain
proud
ride
rice
right
rent
raise

When you say the word **wheel**, the **w** and **h** sounds blend together to make the **wh** sound. Find each **wh** word below to fill the clown's wheelbarrow.

wheat
wheel
white
the
there
shy
phone
share
whistle
whale

When you say the word **prince**, the **p** and the **r** sounds blend together. Help the prince find the prize by following the path of words that begin with the **pr** sound.

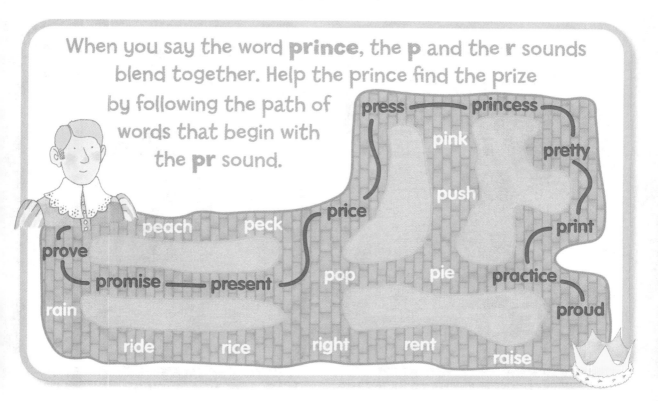

press — princess — pretty
pink
push
pretty
print
price
peach   peck
prove
promise — present
pop   pie   practice
proud
rain
ride   rice   right   rent
raise

When you say the word **wheel**, the **w** and **h** sounds blend together to make the **wh** sound. Find each **wh** word below to fill the clown's wheelbarrow.

wheat   wheel   white
the   there
shy   phone
share   whistle
whale

Questions

Which letter comes next? Use the picture to help.

no__

What sound does the letter **K** make? Does this picture begin with the letter **K**?

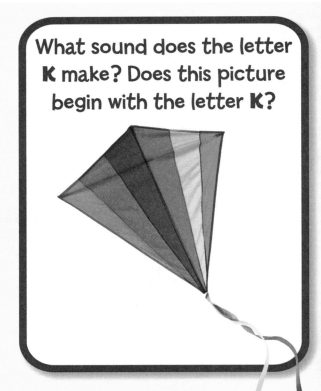

When you say the word **plane**, the **p** and the **l** sounds blend together. Find words that begin with the **pl** sound.

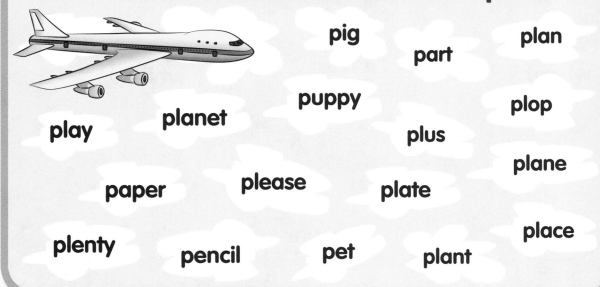

pig   plan

part

puppy   plop

planet   plus

play   plane

paper   please   plate

place

plenty   pencil   pet   plant

Answers

Which letter comes next? Use the picture to help.

n o p

What sound does the letter **K** make? Does this picture begin with the letter **K**?

Yes, kite begins with K.

When you say the word **plane**, the **p** and the **l** sounds blend together. Find words that begin with the **pl** sound.

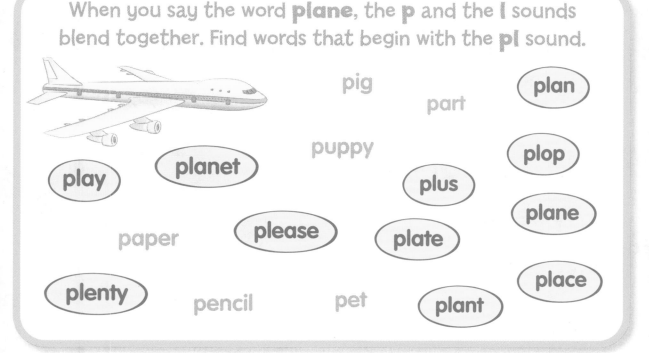

pig

part

plan

puppy

plop

play

planet

plus

plane

please

plate

paper

place

plenty

pencil

pet

plant

Which letter comes first? Use the picture to help.

_rs

Find the sight words **is** and **me**.

lost	chick	he
cow	run	mop	pat
is	farm	horse
dry	eat	fly	top
daisy	am	cake
you	too	me	try

Which words in this sentence begin with the letter **J**?

In January, Joyce wears a jeweled jacket.

Which of these things begin with the letter **M**?

Which letter comes first?
Use the picture to help.

q r s

Find the sight words
is and **me**.

lost	chick	he
cow	run mop	pat
(is)	farm	horse
dry	eat	fly	top
daisy	am	cake
you	too	(me)	try

Which words in this
sentence begin with
the letter **J**?

In **January,**
Joyce wears a
jeweled jacket.

Which of these things
begin with the letter **M**?

magnet

Which words in this sentence begin with the letter **L**?

Let's lounge on the lawn after lunch.

Which of these things begin with the letter **N**?

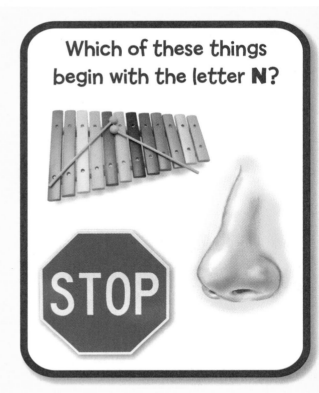

The letter **A** can make a short **A** sound, like in **wagon**. Add an **A** to each space to make words with a short **A** sound.

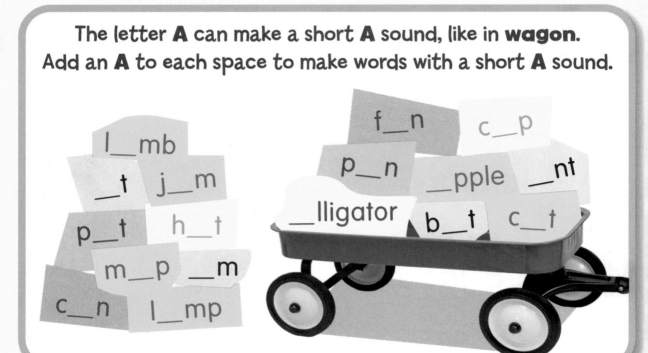

l__mb

_t j__m

p__t h__t

m__p __m

c__n l__mp

f__n c__p

p__n __pple __nt

__lligator b__t c__t

Which words in this sentence begin with the letter **L**?

Let's lounge on the **lawn** after **lunch**.

Which of these things begin with the letter **N**?

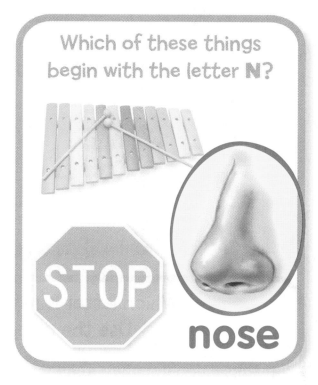

nose

The letter **A** can make a short **A** sound, like in **wagon**. Add an **A** to each space to make words with a short **A** sound.

l a mb

a t   j a m

p a t   h a t

m a p   a m

c a n   l a mp

f a n   c a p

p a n   a pple   a nt

a lligator   b a t   c a t

Questions

Say the word for each picture.
Which words belong in the **ine** word family?

Which letter is missing from each word?
Use the pictures to help you.

__ar   __angaroo   __emon

Say the word for each picture.
Which words belong in the **at** word family?

Say the word for each picture.
Which words belong in the **ine** word family?

nine

vine

Which letter is missing from each word?
Use the pictures to help you.

<u>j</u>ar <u>k</u>angaroo <u>l</u>emon

Say the word for each picture.
Which words belong in the **at** word family?

cat

bat

What sound does the letter **L** make? Does this picture begin with the letter **L**?

Which words in this sentence begin with the letter **M**?

My mother makes muffins on Mondays.

Which of these things begin with the letter **P**?

Which letter comes next? Use the picture to help.

pq__

What sound does the letter **L** make? Does this picture begin with the letter **L**?

Yes, lizard begins with L.

Which words in this sentence begin with the letter **M**?

My mother makes muffins on Mondays.

Which of these things begin with the letter **P**?

pineapple

panda

Which letter comes next? Use the picture to help.

p q r

Questions

Say the word for each picture.
Which words belong in the **ock** word family?

Complete the sentence with a word
that begins with the **tr** sound.

The _____ picked
up passengers at the
station.

Say the word for each picture.
Which words belong in the **ump** word family?

Say the word for each picture.
Which words belong in the **ock** word family?

sock

clock

Complete the sentence with a word
that begins with the **tr** sound.

The ___**train**___ picked
up passengers at the
station.

Say the word for each picture.
Which words belong in the **ump** word family?

pumpkin

stump

Question

When you say the word **brick**, the **b** and the **r** sounds blend together. Find the words in the bricks that begin with the **br** sound to help guide the kitty down the wall.

brake	bed	read	eat
ground	brown	round	bow
room	boom	breath	snow
roar	brave	easy	rain
barn	rat	bridge	reach
father	sister	mother	brother

Answer

When you say the word **brick**, the **b** and the **r** sounds blend together. Find the words in the bricks that begin with the **br** sound to help guide the kitty down the wall.

brake · bed · read · eat

ground · brown · round · bow

room · boom · breath · snow

roar · brave · easy · rain

barn · rat · bridge · reach

father · sister · mother · brother

Find the sight words **like** and **play**.

bat	go	off	won
like	up	water	
so	lap	net	cop
hairy	play		or
tap	the	for	bite
do	kitten	dog	

What sound does the letter **M** make? Does this picture begin with the letter **M**?

Which words in this sentence begin with the letter **N**?

Nick never found the note that Nancy sent.

Which of these things begin with the letter **Q**?

Find the sight words **like** and **play**.

bat	go	off	won
(like)	up	water	
so	lap	net	cop
hairy	(play)	or	
tap	the	for	bite
do	kitten	dog	

What sound does the letter **M** make? Does this picture begin with the letter **M**?

Yes, monkey begins with M.

Which words in this sentence begin with the letter **N**?

Nick never found the note that Nancy sent.

Which of these things begin with the letter **Q**?

quarter

Questions

Say the word for each picture.
Which words belong in the **ake** word family?

Which letter is missing from each word?
Use the pictures to help you.

__uice   __eys   __ion

Say the word for each picture.
Which words belong in the **ing** word family?

Say the word for each picture.
Which words belong in the **ake** word family?

cake

shake

Which letter is missing from each word?
Use the pictures to help you.

__j__ uice   __k__ eys   __l__ ion

---

king

Say the word for each picture.
Which words belong in the **ing** word family?

ring

Questions

What sound does the letter **N** make? Does this picture begin with the letter **N**?

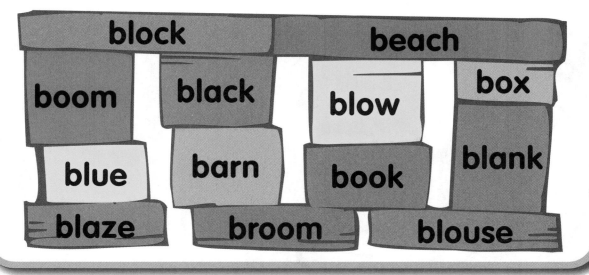

Which words in this sentence begin with the letter **P**?

The pink posy plant costs a pretty penny.

When you say the word **block**, the **b** and the **l** sounds blend together. Look at the word in each block. Which words have the **bl** sound?

block

beach

boom

black

blow

box

blue

barn

book

blank

blaze

broom

blouse

What sound does the letter **N** make? Does this picture begin with the letter **N**?

No, rabbit begins with R.

Which words in this sentence begin with the letter **P**?

The **pink posy plant** costs a **pretty penny**.

When you say the word **block**, the **b** and the **l** sounds blend together. Look at the word in each block. Which words have the **bl** sound?

block

beach

boom

black

blow

box

blue

barn

book

blank

blaze

broom

blouse

Which letter comes next? Use the picture to help.

q r __

Which words in this sentence begin with the letter **Q**?

Quickly tell the queen that the quest is over!

Which of these things begin with the letter **R**?

Say the word for the picture. Which sound do you hear at the beginning?

j h g

Which letter comes next? Use the picture to help.

q r s

Which words in this sentence begin with the letter **Q**?

Quickly tell the **queen** that the **quest** is over!

Which of these things begin with the letter **R**?

rug

rabbit

Say the word for the picture. Which sound do you hear at the beginning?

jar

j h g

Question

When you say the word **glow**, the **g** and the **l** sounds blend together. Look at the journal entry below. Which words begin with the **gl** sound?

February 15

Last night, it snowed!
The snow glows in the morning sun.
The sun gleams off the snow.
The icy lake looks like glass.
The snow clings to tree branches.
It is like they are stuck there with glue!
I'm so glad it snowed!

When you say the word **glow**, the **g** and the **l** sounds blend together. Look at the journal entry below. Which words begin with the **gl** sound?

February 15

Last night, it snowed!
The snow (glows) in the morning sun.
The sun (gleams) off the snow.
The icy lake looks like (glass)
The snow clings to tree branches.
It is like they are stuck there with (glue)
I'm so (glad) it snowed!

Which words in this sentence begin with the letter **R**?

The race was really fun for each runner.

What sound does the letter **P** make? Does this picture begin with the letter **P**?

Which letter comes next? Use the picture to help.

rs___

Which of these things begin with the letter **S**?

Which words in this sentence begin with the letter **R**?

The **race** was **really** fun for each **runner**.

What sound does the letter **P** make? Does this picture begin with the letter **P**?

Yes, pig begins with P.

Which letter comes next? Use the picture to help.

rs t

Which of these things begin with the letter **S**?

socks

sunglasses

Questions

Say the word for each picture.
Which words belong in the **ide** word family?

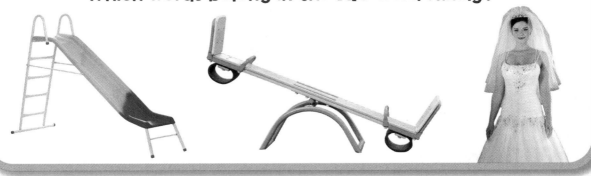

Which letter is missing from each word?
Use the pictures to help you.

__acket   __id   __obster

Say the word for each picture.
Which words belong in the **ain** word family?

Answers

Say the word for each picture.
Which words belong in the **ide** word family?

slide

bride

Which letter is missing from each word?
Use the pictures to help you.

jacket   **k** id   **l**obster

Say the word for each picture.
Which words belong in the **ain** word family? **train**

chain

Questions

Which letter comes next? Use the picture to help.

tu___

Which words in this sentence begin with the letter **S**?

There are seven seashells on the sandy seashore.

When you say the word **star**, the **s** and the **t** sounds blend together. Say the word for each picture. Which words have the **st** sound?

Which letter comes next? Use the picture to help.

t u **v**

Which words in this sentence begin with the letter **S**?

There are **seven seashells** on the **sandy seashore**.

When you say the word **star**, the **s** and the **t** sounds blend together. Say the word for each picture. Which words have the **st** sound?

stamp

stump

stool

stop

Which of these things begin with the letter **T**?

Which words in this sentence begin with the letter **T**?

The track team practiced for two hours.

When you say the word **mask**, the **s** and the **k** sounds blend together. Point to the masks that have a word with the **sk** sound.

mask mast

rise risk

ask asp

dish disk

dusk dust

tack task

Which of these things begin with the letter **T**?

tomato

turtle

Which words in this sentence begin with the letter **T**?

The track team practiced for two hours.

When you say the word **mask**, the **s** and the **k** sounds blend together. Point to the masks that have a word with the **sk** sound.

mask mast rise risk ask asp

dish disk dusk dust tack task

Questions

Which of these things begin with the letter **V**?

What sound does the letter **Q** make? Does this picture begin with the letter **Q**?

When you say the word **spy**, the **s** and the **p** sounds blend together. Which words below have the **sp** sound?

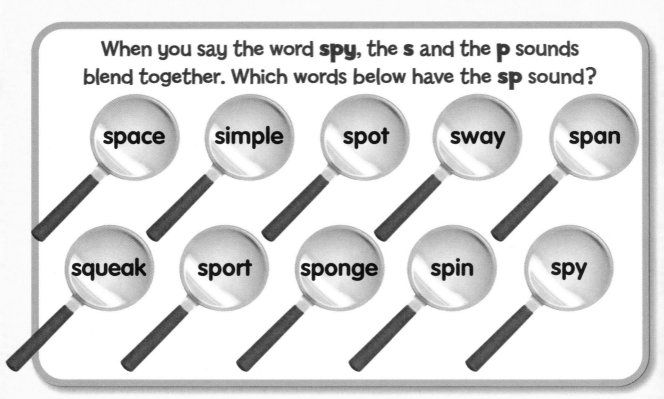

space   simple   spot   sway   span

squeak   sport   sponge   spin   spy

Which of these things begin with the letter **V**?

violin

vest

What sound does the letter **Q** make? Does this picture begin with the letter **Q**?

Yes, queen begins with Q.

When you say the word **spy**, the **s** and the **p** sounds blend together. Which words below have the **sp** sound?

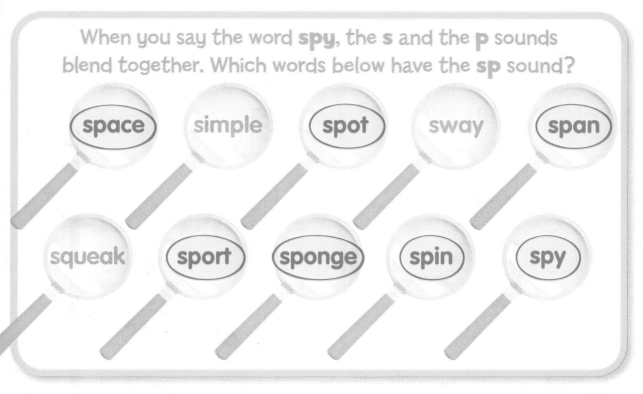

space   simple   spot   sway   span

squeak   sport   sponge   spin   spy

What sound does the letter **R** make? Does this picture begin with the letter **R**?

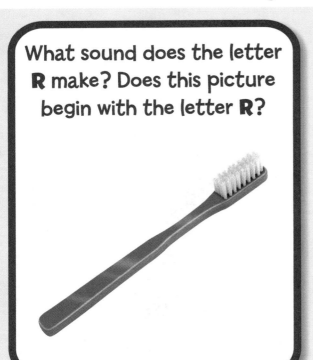

Which words in this sentence begin with the letter **V**?

Vivian's voice was very pretty with the violin.

Say the word for the picture. Which sound do you hear at the beginning?

g h k

Which of these things begin with the letter **W**?

What sound does the letter **R** make? Does this picture begin with the letter **R**?

No, toothbrush begins with T.

Which words in this sentence begin with the letter **V**?

Vivian's voice was very pretty with the violin.

Say the word for the picture. Which sound do you hear at the beginning?

kitten

g h (k)

Which of these things begin with the letter **W**?

watermelon

whale

Question

The letter **U** can make a short **U** sound, like in **bus**.
Draw a line following each word that has a
short **U** sound to get the bus to school.

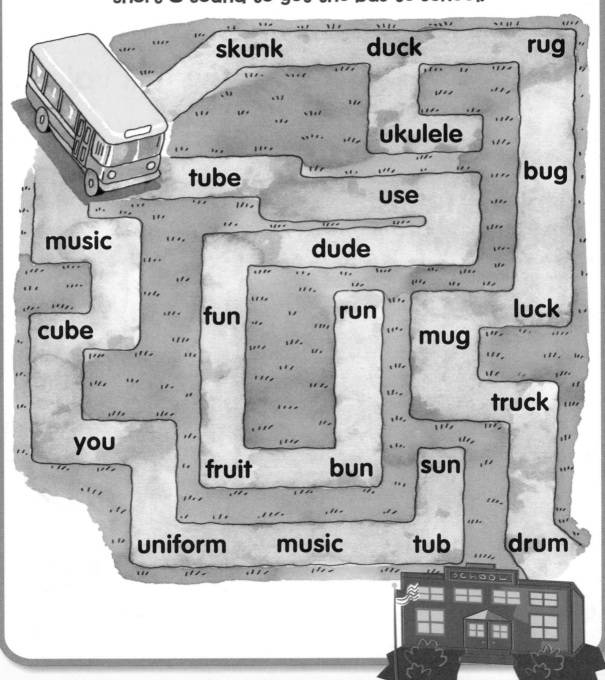

Answer

The letter **U** can make a short **U** sound, like in **bus**.
Draw a line following each word that has a
short **U** sound to get the bus to school.

skunk — duck — rug

ukulele

tube

use

bug

music

dude

cube

fun   run   luck

mug

you

truck

fruit   bun   sun

uniform   music   tub   drum

Which word in this sentence begins with the letter **X**?

Suzie needs an X-ray of her arm.

What sound does the letter **S** make? Does this picture begin with the letter **S**?

Which letter comes next? Use the picture to help.

U V ___

Which of these things begin with the letter **X**?

Which word in this sentence begins with the letter **X**?

Suzie needs an **X-ray** of her arm.

What sound does the letter **S** make? Does this picture begin with the letter **S**?

Yes, sun begins with S.

Which letter comes next? Use the picture to help.

U V **W**

Which of these things begin with the letter **X**?

xylophone

Questions

Which letter is missing from each word?
Use the pictures to help you.

__usic   __est   __ig

Say the word for each picture.
Which words belong in the **ell** word family?

Which letter is missing from each word?
Use the pictures to help you.

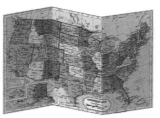  

__ap   __ose   __encil

Which letter is missing from each word?
Use the pictures to help you.

music   **n** est   **p** ig

Say the word for each picture.
Which words belong in the **ell** word family? **bell**

shell

Which letter is missing from each word?
Use the pictures to help you.

map   **n** ose   **p** encil

What sound does the letter **T** make? Does this picture begin with the letter **T**?

Which words in this sentence begin with the letter **W**?

Willy was a wonderful worker every Wednesday.

Which of these things begin with the letter **Z**?

Which letter comes next? Use the picture to help.

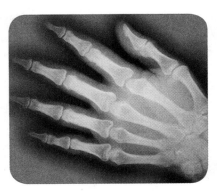

V W ___

What sound does the letter **T** make? Does this picture begin with the letter **T**?

Yes, tiger begins with T.

Which words in this sentence begin with the letter **W**?

Willy was a wonderful worker every Wednesday.

Which of these things begin with the letter **Z**?

zebra

Which letter comes next? Use the picture to help.

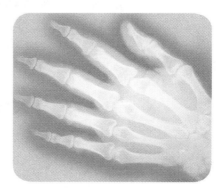

V W X

Questions

Which words in this sentence begin with the letter **y**?

Your friend yodeled in my yard yesterday.

Point to the silent **E** in this word.

ape

The letter **A** can make a long **A** sound, like in **rain**. Say the word in each raindrop. Point to the raindrops that have words with a long **A** sound.

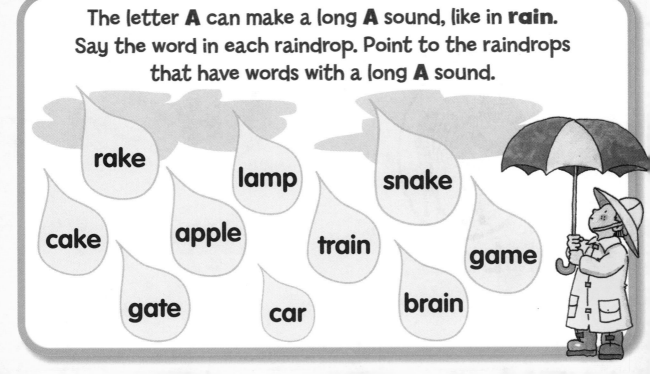

rake

lamp

snake

cake

apple

train

game

gate

car

brain

Which words in this sentence begin with the letter **y**?

Your friend **yodeled** in my **yard yesterday**.

Point to the silent **E** in this word.

ape

The letter **A** can make a long **A** sound, like in **rain**. Say the word in each raindrop. Point to the raindrops that have words with a long **A** sound.

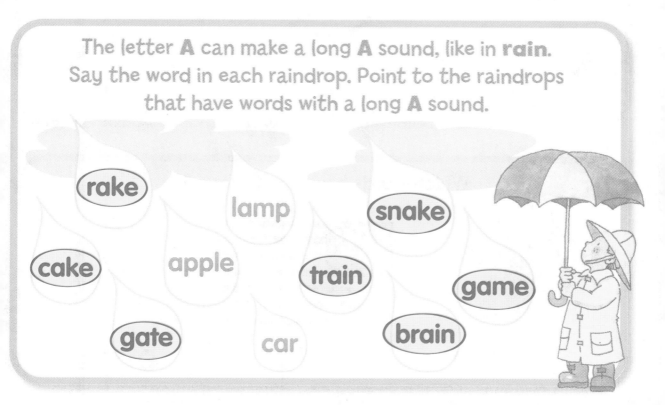

rake

lamp

snake

cake

apple

train

game

gate

car

brain

Questions

Say the word for each picture.
Which words belong in the **uck** word family?

Which letter is missing from each word?
Use the pictures to help you.

__edal   __ails   __arrot

Which words have the **fl** sound?

__ower   __ag   __eather

Answers

Say the word for each picture.
Which words belong in the **uck** word family?

duck **truck**

Which letter is missing from each word?
Use the pictures to help you.

medal   **n** ails   **p** arrot

Which words have the **fl** sound?

fl ower   **fl** ag   ___eather

Which letter comes next? Use the picture to help.

W X __

Which words in this sentence begin with the letter **Z**?

Zack saw zero hippos at the zoo.

How many of these things start with the letter **y**?

What sound does the letter **V** make? Does this picture begin with the letter **V**?

Which letter comes next?
Use the picture to help.

w x _y_

Which words in this sentence begin with the letter **Z**?

Zack saw zero hippos at the zoo.

How many of these things start with the letter **Y**?

yak

yo-yo

What sound does the letter **V** make? Does this picture begin with the letter **V**?

Yes, vase begins with V.

Question

The letter **E** can make a long **E** sound, like in **bee**.
Add an **E** to each space to make words with a long **E** sound.

__agle

tr_____

qu___n

b__agle

f____t

j__ans

s__al

The letter **E** can make a long **E** sound, like in **bee**.
Add an **E** to each space to make words with a long **E** sound.

_e_ agle

tr _e_ e

qu _e_ _e_ n

b _e_ agle

fe _e_ t

j _e_ ans

s _e_ al

Which letter is missing from each word?
Use the pictures to help you.

__uilt

__ice

__nowman

Which word matches
the picture?

sing

ring

ding

Which word matches
the picture?

rake

cake

cane

Which letter is missing from each word?
Use the pictures to help you.

q uilt

r ice

s nowman

Which word matches
the picture?

sing

(ring)

ding

Which word matches
the picture?

rake

(cake)

cane

Questions

Point to the silent **E** in this word.

apple

Sometimes the letter **y** can sound like the letter **E**. Which word below has a **y** that makes an **E** sound?

yo-yo

pony

Say the word for the picture. Which sound do you hear at the beginning?

g h k

What sound does the letter **W** make? Does this picture begin with the letter **W**?

Point to the silent **E** in this word.

apple

Sometimes the letter **y** can sound like the letter **E**. Which word below has a **y** that makes an **E** sound?

yo-yo

pony

Say the word for the picture. Which sound do you hear at the beginning?

hat

g (h) k

What sound does the letter **W** make? Does this picture begin with the letter **W**?

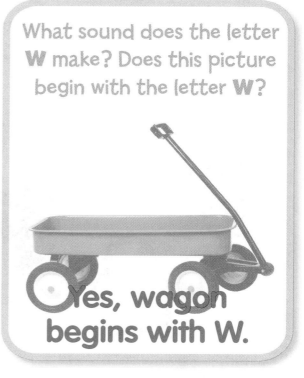

Yes, wagon begins with W.

Questions

Add a silent **E** to
change the word.
What is the new word?

can__

Find the sight word
can in the puzzle.

a n b c l
e f r a p
t v s n w
y z h x o
w p m i t

The letter **O** can make a short sound, like in **box**.
Say the word for each picture. Which words have a short **O**?

Add a silent **E** to change the word. What is the new word?

can**e**

Find the sight word **can** in the puzzle.

a n b c l
e f r a p
t v s n w
y z h x o
w p m i t

The letter **O** can make a short sound, like in **box**. Say the word for each picture. Which words have a short **O**?

mop

frog

lock

doll

Questions

Say the letter **X** out loud.
Does this picture begin with
the letter **X**?

Add a silent **E** to
change the word.
What is the new word?

cub__

Which word has a
short **A** vowel sound?

cap
cape

Which letter is missing?
Use the picture to help you.

xy__

Say the letter **X** out loud.
Does this picture begin with
the letter **X**?

**No, flower
begins with F.**

Add a silent **E** to
change the word.
What is the new word?

cub<u>e</u>

Which word has a
short **A** vowel sound?

cap

cape

Which letter is missing?
Use the picture to help you.

xy <u>z</u>

Say the word for each picture.
Which words belong in the **est** word family?

Which picture matches the word?

shoe

Which word matches the picture?

net
night
neat

Say the word for each picture.
Which words belong in the **est** word family?

vest

nest

Which picture matches
the word?

shoe

Which word matches
the picture?

net

night

neat

Questions

Which word rhymes with this picture?

fire   water

Point to the silent **E** in this word.

fire

What sound does the letter **y** make? Does this picture begin with the letter **y**?

Which word has a long **A** vowel sound?

cane

can

Which word rhymes
with this picture?

Fire rhymes with tire.

(fire) water

Point to the silent **E**
in this word.

fire

What sound does the letter
y make? Does this picture
begin with the letter **y**?

Yes, yarn
begins with Y.

Which word has a
long **A** vowel sound?

cane

can

Point to the **th** sounds in this sentence.

I tried on these shoes, and then I tried on three more!

Say the word for the picture. What is its beginning sound?

sm   sl   sc

Say the word for each picture. Which one begins with the **sl** sound?

Which picture rhymes with this word?

yarn

Point to the **th** sounds in this sentence.

I tried on **these** shoes, and **then** I tried on **three** more!

Say the word for the picture. What is its beginning sound?

(**sm**) sl   sc

smile

Say the word for each picture. Which one begins with the **sl** sound?

slide

Which picture rhymes with this word?

yarn

barn

Questions

Point to the words in this sentence with an **aw** sound.

There was a fawn on the lawn at dawn.

Add a silent **E** to make a word. What is the word?

lim__

The letter **O** can make a long **O** sound, like in **goat**. Find pictures with a long **O** sound.

Point to the words in this sentence with an **aw** sound.

There was a fawn on the lawn at dawn.

Add a silent **E** to make a word. What is the word?

lime

The letter **O** can make a long **O** sound, like in **goat**. Find pictures with a long **O** sound.

goat

boat

soap

rope

Pair the letter **a** with the letter **r** to create an **ar** sound, like in shark. Match each picture to the correct **ar** word.

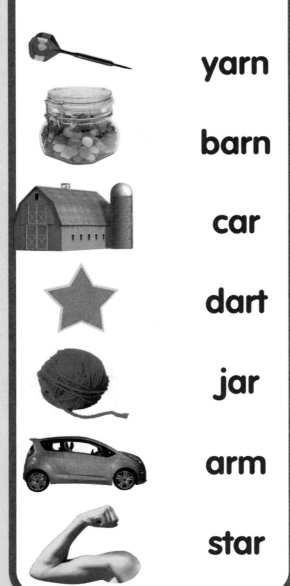

yarn

barn

car

dart

jar

arm

star

Find the words with a short **I** sound.

brick

tiger

fish

chick

time

ice

pin

Answers

Pair the letter **a** with the letter **r** to create an **ar** sound, like in shark. Match each picture to the correct **ar** word.

yarn

barn

car

dart

jar

arm

star

Find the words with a short **I** sound.

brick

tiger

fish

chick

time

ice

pin

Find the sight word **and** in the puzzle.

t	c	w	o	q
c	x	m	t	a
m	h	k	i	e
o	a	n	d	u
p	q	z	v	g

What sound does the letter **Z** make? Does this picture begin with the letter **Z**?

Point to the silent **E** in this word.

time

Which word rhymes with this picture?

moon   star

Find the sight word **and** in the puzzle.

t	c	w	o	q
c	x	m	t	a
m	h	k	i	e
o	**a**	**n**	**d**	u
p	q	z	v	g

What sound does the letter **Z** make? Does this picture begin with the letter **Z**?

No, kiwi begins with K.

Point to the silent **E** in this word.

time

Which word rhymes with this picture?

Moon rhymes with spoon.

moon star

Questions

Say the word for the picture. Which sound do you hear at the beginning?

j g h

Say the word for each picture. Which pictures have an **ar** sound?

The letter **U** can make a long **U** sound, like in **unicorn**. Choose the long **U** word under each picture.

cube   cub

tub   tube

umbrella   uniform

unicycle   uncle

Say the word for the picture. Which sound do you hear at the beginning?

grapes

j (**g**) h

Say the word for each picture. Which pictures have an **ar** sound?

star

car

The letter **U** can make a long **U** sound, like in **unicorn**. Choose the long **U** word under each picture.

(**cube**) cub

tub (**tube**)

umbrella (**uniform**) (**unicycle**) uncle

Which letter is missing from each word?
Use the pictures to help you.

__uail   __ose   __ix

Which word matches
the picture?

nest

best

rest

Which word matches
the picture?

leap

lets

lips

Which letter is missing from each word?
Use the pictures to help you.

q uail   **r** ose   **s** ix

Which word matches
the picture?

nest

best

rest

Which word matches
the picture?

leap

lets

lips

Add a silent **E** to change the word. What is the new word?

kit__

Which picture rhymes with this word?

pie

Say the word for the picture. What is its beginning sound?

st   sw   sh

Point to the silent **E** in this word.

smile

Add a silent **E** to change the word. What is the new word?

kit_e_

Which picture rhymes with this word?

pie

tie

Say the word for the picture. What is its beginning sound?

st   sw   (sh)

sheep

Point to the silent **E** in this word.

smile

Say the word for each picture.
Which words belong in the **ight** word family?

Which word matches
the picture?

line
lime
lean

Which word matches
the picture?

bell
fell
tall

Answers

Say the word for each picture.
Which words belong in the **ight** word family?

night light

Which word matches
the picture?

line
lime
lean

Which word matches
the picture?

bell
fell
tall

Add a silent **E** to change the word. What is the new word?

man___

Which word has a short **E** vowel sound?

set

seat

Find the sight word **see** in the puzzle.

n s e e o
r h a p k
a z f i d
b c v m h
w d x g a

Which word rhymes with this picture?

dog   cat

Add a silent **E** to change the word. What is the new word?

man__e__

Which word has a short **E** vowel sound?

set

seat

Find the sight word **see** in the puzzle.

n (s e e) o
r h a p k
a z f i d
b c v m h
w d x g a

Which word rhymes with this picture?

Dog rhymes with frog.

 cat

Questions

Say the word for each picture. Which picture begins with the **sp** sound?

Sometimes the letter **y** can sound like the letter **E**. Which word below has a **y** that makes an **E** sound?

yolk

sunny

Which word has a long **E** vowel sound?

bee

bet

Say the word for each picture. Which picture has an **er** sound?

Say the word for each picture. Which picture begins with the **sp** sound?

spoon

Sometimes the letter **y** can sound like the letter **E**. Which word below has a **y** that makes an **E** sound?

yolk

sunny

Which word has a long **E** vowel sound?

bee

bet

Say the word for each picture. Which picture has an **er** sound?

flower

Questions

When you say the word **snap**, the **s** and the **n** sounds blend together. Say the word for each picture. Which words begin with the **sn** sound?

____**eep**　　____**oon**　　____**ake**

____**eeze**　　____**ail**　　____**ore**

When you say the word **grand**, the **g** and the **r** sounds blend together. Help complete this letter by choosing words that begin with the **gr** sound.

Dear (Grandma, Mom) and (Dad, Grandpa),

Thank you for my birthday gift!
How did you know I wanted a (goat, grasshopper)?
He is really (great, good)!
He is (green, red).
He likes to eat (cookies, grass)!
I wonder how big he will (get, grow)?

Your (grandson, girl),
(Greg, George)

When you say the word **snap**, the **s** and the **n** sounds blend together. Say the word for each picture. Which words begin with the **sn** sound?

 ____eep

 ____oon

 sn ake

 **sn** eeze

 **sn** ail

 **sn** ore

When you say the word **grand**, the **g** and the **r** sounds blend together. Help complete this letter by choosing words that begin with the **gr** sound.

Dear (Grandma) Mom) and (Dad, Grandpa)

Thank you for my birthday gift!
How did you know I wanted a (goat, grasshopper)?
He is really (great, good)!
He is (green, red).
He likes to eat (cookies, grass)
I wonder how big he will (get, grow)?

Your (grandson, girl),
(Greg, George)

Questions

Which word rhymes with this picture?

cat   bed

Which word has a short **I** vowel sound?

kit

kite

Which **sw** word would you say in this sentence?

The white

_____

floats on the lake.

swan   swim

Which of these things start with the **ch** sound?

Which word rhymes with this picture?

Cat rhymes with hat.

(cat) **bed**

Which word has a short **I** vowel sound?

kite

Which **sw** word would you say in this sentence?

The white

_____

floats on the lake.

Which of these things start with the **ch** sound?

cheese

Questions

Which letter is missing from each word?
Use the pictures to help you.

__ueen   __ing   __oap

Which word matches
the picture?

boat

coat

bat

Which picture matches
the word?

dog

Which letter is missing from each word?
Use the pictures to help you.

_q ueen   **_r** ing   **_s** oap

Which word matches the picture?

boat
coat
bat

Which picture matches the word?

dog

Find the sight word **for** in the puzzle.

a	l	p	f	d
f	o	r	i	e
h	r	y	b	h
e	w	n	g	q
k	u	c	b	k

Which of these things begins with the **sn** sound?

Say the word for the picture. What is its beginning sound?

ch   **cr**   **cl**

Sometimes the letter **y** can sound like the letter **E**. Which word below has a **y** that makes an **E** sound?

yellow

bunny

Find the sight word **for** in the puzzle.

a   l   p   f   d

(f   o   r) i   e

h   r   y   b   h

e   w   n   g   q

k   u   c   b   k

Which of these things begins with the **sn** sound?

snail

Say the word for the picture. What is its beginning sound?

(**ch**)   cr   cl

chair

Sometimes the letter **y** can sound like the letter **E**. Which word below has a **y** that makes an **E** sound?

yellow

(**bunny**)

Question

The letter **I** can make a long **I** sound, like in **lime**.
Say the name of the pictures in each row.
Which ones have a long **I** sound?

The letter **I** can make a long **I** sound, like in **lime**.
Say the name of the pictures in each row.
Which ones have a long **I** sound?

 **dime**

  **five**

  **kite**

  **nine**

 **lime**

Say the word for each picture.
Which sound blend is missing from each word?

  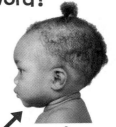

___**over**   ___**ayons**   ___**in**

When you say the word **thank**, the **t** and **h** sounds blend together to make the **th** sound. Match each **th** word to the correct picture.

thirteen   **thimble**   **thirty**

thumb   **thread**

Say the word for each picture.
Which sound blend is missing from each word?

 **cl** over

 **cr** ayons

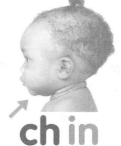 **ch** in

When you say the word **thank**, the **t** and **h**
sounds blend together to make the **th** sound.
Match each **th** word to the correct picture.

thirteen **thumb** **thimble** **thread** **thirty**

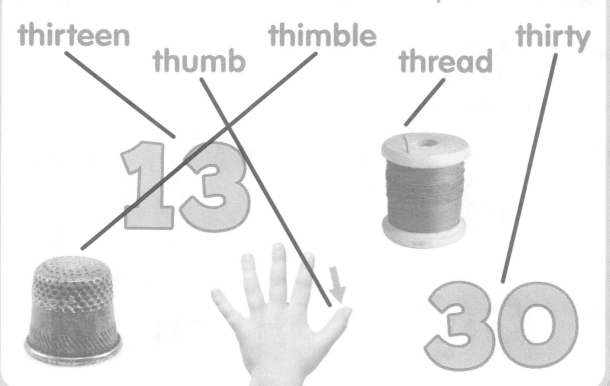

Say the word for each picture. Which one begins with a **wh** sound?

Which picture rhymes with this word?

bell

Which word has a long **I** vowel sound?

pie
pig

Which words end with the **st** sound?

Say the word for each picture. Which one begins with a **wh** sound?

whale

Which picture rhymes with this word?

bell

shell

Which word has a long **I** vowel sound?

pie

pig

Which words end with the **st** sound?

vest

nest

Which word has a short **o** vowel sound?

cop
coat

Which word rhymes with this picture?

box   **case**

Which pictures begin with the **cl** sound?

Find the sight word **the** in the puzzle.

g o r w z
a p s x l
t f o t c
h i q e n
e w y b u

Which word has a
short **o** vowel sound?

cop

coat

Which word rhymes
with this picture?

Box rhymes with fox.

box   case

Which pictures begin
with the **cl** sound?

cloud

clown

Find the sight word **the**
in the puzzle.

g o r w z
a p s x l
t f o t c
h i q e n
e w y b u

Sometimes the letter **y** can sound like the letter **E**. Which word below has a **y** that makes an **E** sound?

yams

puppy

Say the word for the picture. What is its beginning sound?

cl   bl   pl

Say the word for each picture. Which pictures have an **ur** sound?

Which word rhymes with this picture?

sled   ball

Sometimes the letter **y** can sound like the letter **E**. Which word below has a **y** that makes an **E** sound?

yams

puppy

Say the word for the picture. What is its beginning sound?

cl bl pl

cloud

Say the word for each picture. Which pictures have an **ur** sound?

surfer

purse

Which word rhymes with this picture?

Sled rhymes with bed.

sled ball

When you say the word **train**, the **t** and the **r** sounds blend together. Say the word for the each picture. Point to the words with the **tr** sound.

The sound blends **ou** and **ow** can have similar sounds, like in **couch** and **clown**. Point to the word under each picture that is spelled correctly.

howse
house

crown
croun

couch
cowch

cloun
clown

When you say the word **train**, the **t** and the **r** sounds blend together. Say the word for the each picture. Point to the words with the **tr** sound.

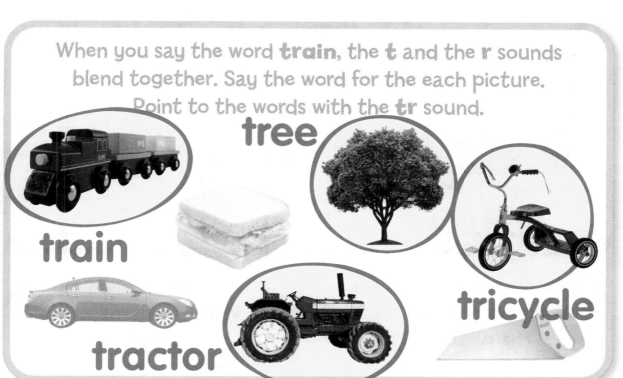

tree

train

tricycle

tractor

The sound blends **ou** and **ow** can have similar sounds, like in **couch** and **clown**. Point to the word under each picture that is spelled correctly.

howse
house

crown
croun

couch
cowch

cloun
clown

Which letter is missing from each word?
Use the pictures to help you.

__oolbox   __ine   __ater

Which word matches the picture?

scarf

hat

glove

Which word matches the picture?

mope

mop

moat

Which letter is missing from each word?
Use the pictures to help you.

toolbox   **v**ine   **w**ater

Which word matches
the picture?

scarf

hat

glove

Which word matches
the picture?

mope

mop

moat

Say the word for the picture. What is its beginning sound?

cl   bl   pl

Which picture rhymes with this word?

rake

Which picture begins with the **dr** sound?

Which word has a long **O** vowel sound?

dot

boat

Say the word for the picture. What is its beginning sound?

cl   bl   (pl)

plant

Which picture rhymes with this word?

rake
snake

Which picture begins with the **dr** sound?

drum

Which word has a long **o** vowel sound?

dot

boat

Find the sight word **has** in the puzzle.

q g d y u
u h e s r
w p r f h
y e m u a
c z o p s

Which pictures begin with the **gl** sound?

Say the word for each picture. Which picture has an **oo** sound?

Which word rhymes with this picture?

star   **sun**

Answers

Find the sight word **has** in the puzzle.

q	g	d	y	u
u	h	e	s	r
w	p	r	f	**h**
y	e	m	u	**a**
c	z	o	p	**s**

Which pictures begin with the **gl** sound?

glasses

globe

Say the word for each picture. Which picture has an **oo** sound?

boot

Which word rhymes with this picture?

Star rhymes with car.

star   sun

Questions

Which letter is missing from each word?
Use the pictures to help you.

  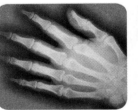

__ote   __olf   __-ray

Which word matches the picture?

track

truck

trek

Which word matches the picture?

sat

mat

cat

Which letter is missing from each word?
Use the pictures to help you.

 **v**ote

 **w**olf

 **X**-ray

Which word matches
the picture?

track

truck

trek

Which word matches
the picture?

sat

mat

cat

Questions

Which word has a short U vowel sound?

tub

tube

Which picture rhymes with this word?

bear

Which pictures begin with the cr sound?

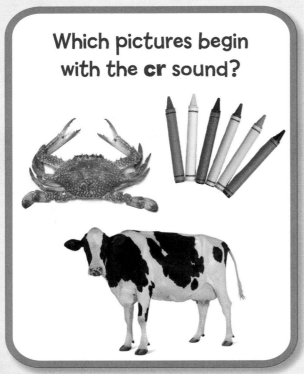

Say the word for the picture. What is its beginning sound?

al   cl   el

Which word has a short U vowel sound?

tub

tube

Which picture rhymes with this word?

bear
chair

Which pictures begin with the cr sound?

crab

crayons

Say the word for the picture. What is its beginning sound?

al **cl** el

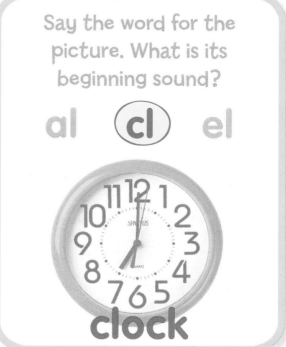

clock

Questions

Which word rhymes with this picture?

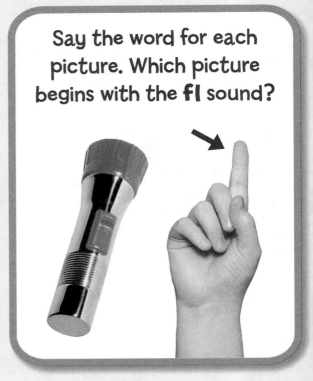

swing   slide

Say the word for each picture. Which picture begins with the fl sound?

Say the word for each picture. Which picture has an aw sound?

Sometimes the letter y can sound like the letter E. Which word below has a y that makes an E sound?

money

yarn

Which word rhymes with this picture?

Swing rhymes with ring.

swing slide

Say the word for each picture. Which picture begins with the **fl** sound?

flashlight

Say the word for each picture. Which picture has an **aw** sound?

saw

Sometimes the letter **y** can sound like the letter **E**. Which word below has a **y** that makes an **E** sound?

money

yarn

Questions

Which letter is missing from each word?
Use the pictures to help you.

__ail   __iolin   __ing

Which picture matches
the word?

ear

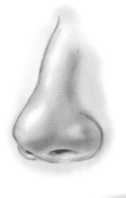
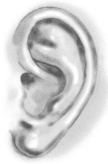

Which word matches
the picture?

kites
keys
keep

Answers

Which letter is missing from each word?
Use the pictures to help you.

t ail

v iolin

w ing

Which picture matches the word?

ear

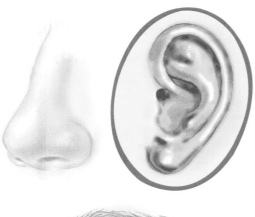

Which word matches the picture?

kites

keys

keep

Questions

Say the word for the picture. What is its beginning sound?

br   gr   cr

Which word rhymes with this picture?

goat   bear

Which picture starts with the **pr** sound?

Which word has a long **U** vowel sound?

tune

under

Say the word for the picture. What is its beginning sound?

br gr cr

bread

Which word rhymes with this picture?

Goat rhymes with boat.

goat **bear**

Which picture starts with the **pr** sound?

present

Which word has a long **U** vowel sound?

tune

under

Questions

Which letter is missing from each word?
Use the pictures to help you.

__ylophone   __ak   __ipper

Which picture matches the word?

bee

Which word matches the picture?

pamper

purple

pumpkin

Which letter is missing from each word?
Use the pictures to help you.

xylophone   **y**ak   **z**ipper

Which picture matches
the word?

bee

Which word matches
the picture?

pamper
purple
pumpkin

Questions

Which word rhymes with this picture?

block brick

Say the word for the number. What is its beginning sound?

th tw tr

12

Which picture rhymes with this word?

hook

Which one of these things begins with the sw sound?

Which word rhymes with this picture?

Block rhymes with clock.

block **brick**

Say the word for the number. What is its beginning sound?

th **tw** tr

twelve

Which picture rhymes with this word?

hook

book

Which one of these things begins with the **sw** sound?

swing

Questions

Which letter is missing from each word?
Use the pictures to help you.

__orm   __ell   __ero

Which picture matches
the word?

bike

Which word matches
the picture?

hat

hate

hard

Which letter is missing from each word?
Use the pictures to help you.

_w orm   **_y** ell   **_z** ero

Which picture matches
the word?

bike

Which word matches
the picture?

hat

hate

hard

Questions

The soft **C** sounds like the letter **S**. Which word has a soft **C** sound?

cake

celery

Say the word for the picture. What is its beginning sound?

br **cr** **gr**

Which picture rhymes with this word?

fun

The soft **G** sounds like the letter **J**. Which word has a soft **G** sound?

bridge

gate

The soft **C** sounds like the letter **S**. Which word has a soft **C** sound?

cake

celery

Say the word for the picture. What is its beginning sound?

br   cr   gr

grass

Which picture rhymes with this word?

fun

sun

The soft **G** sounds like the letter **J**. Which word has a soft **G** sound?

bridge

gate

Point to the words in this sentence that have a soft **C** sound.

The cider costs fifty cents at the county fair.

Which picture rhymes with this word?

wig

Say the word for the picture. What is its beginning sound?

tr   br   cr

Which picture has a hard **C** sound?

cow

city

Point to the words in this sentence that have a soft **C** sound.

The **cider** costs fifty **cents** at the county fair.

Which picture rhymes with this word?

wig

pig

Say the word for the picture. What is its beginning sound?

(**tr**) **br** **cr**

truck

Which picture has a hard **C** sound?

(**cow**)

city

Pair the letter **o** with the letter **r** to create an **or** sound, like in **born**. Match each picture to the correct **or** word.

 corn

 horn

 fork

 story

 acorn

Say the word for the picture. What is its beginning sound?

br   dr   cr

Which picture rhymes with this word?

bee

Pair the letter **o** with the letter **r** to create an **or** sound, like in **born**. Match each picture to the correct **or** word.

corn

horn

fork

story

acorn

Say the word for the picture. What is its beginning sound?

br (dr) cr

dress

Which picture rhymes with this word?

bee

tree

Point to the word in the sentence that has a hard **C** sound.

There is a cactus in the center of the room.

Say the word for the picture. What is its beginning sound?

cr   dr   fr

Which picture starts with a **sh** sound?

Point to the words in this sentence that have a soft **G** sound.

The gerbil is in the orange cage.

Point to the word in the sentence that has a hard **C** sound.

There is a **cactus** in the center of the room.

Say the word for the picture. What is its beginning sound?

cr   dr   (fr)

frog

Which picture starts with a **sh** sound?

shoe

Point to the words in this sentence that have a soft **G** sound.

The **gerbil** is in the **orange cage**.

The letter **E** can make a short **E** sound, like in **sled**. Point to the pictures with the short **E** sound.

The letter **O** can make a long **O** sound, like in **snow**. Find the words below that have a long **O** sound.

crow   row   growl

brow   mow   snow

howl   blow   cow

The letter **E** can make a short **E** sound, like in **sled**. Point to the pictures with the short **E** sound.

ten

sled

red

pen

dress

The letter **O** can make a long **O** sound, like in **snow**. Find the words below that have a long **O** sound.

crow

row

growl

brow

mow

snow

howl

blow

cow

Point to the words in this sentence that have a soft **G** sound.

Gary the giant loves geometry and gymnastics.

Say the word for each picture. Which picture has an **or** sound?

Which picture rhymes with this word?

fall

The soft **G** sounds like the letter **J**. Which word has a soft **G** sound?

gem   gorilla

Point to the words in this sentence that have a soft **G** sound.

Gary the giant loves geometry and gymnastics.

Say the word for each picture. Which picture has an **or** sound?

acorn

Which picture rhymes with this word?

fall

ball

The soft **G** sounds like the letter **J**. Which word has a soft **G** sound?

gem gorilla

The sound blends **sk** and **sc** have similar sounds, like in **skate** and **scarf**. Point to the word under each picture that is spelled correctly.

skate   scate

skarf   scarf

skunk   scunk

The soft **C** sounds like the letter **S**. Which word has a soft **C** sound?

city

coat

Point to the words in the sentence that have a hard **G** sound.

George wants to go to the gym on Gale Street.

The sound blends **sk** and **sc** have similar sounds, like in **skate** and **scarf**. Point to the word under each picture that is spelled correctly.

(skate) scate

skarf (scarf)

(skunk) scunk

The soft **C** sounds like the letter **S**. Which word has a soft **C** sound?

(city)

coat

Point to the words in the sentence that have a hard **G** sound.

George wants to go to the gym on Gale Street.

Which word begins with a hard **C** sound?

carrots

cereal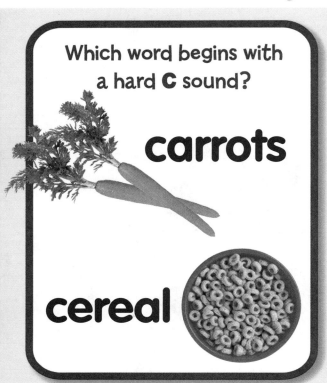

Which word has a hard **G** sound?

goat

badge

Which word has a hard **G** sound?

gold

orange

Point to the word in the sentence that has a hard **C** sound.

Look at the cedar tree by the cabin.

Answers

Which word begins with a hard **C** sound?

carrots

cereal

Which word has a hard **G** sound?

goat

badge

Which word has a hard **G** sound?

gold

orange

Point to the word in the sentence that has a hard **C** sound.

Look at the cedar tree by the **cabin**.

Question

Pair the letter **o** with the letter **y** to create an **oy** sound, like in **boy**. Put the first letter and the letters **oy** together to make new words on the lines below.

b + oy = _____

j + oy = _____

t + oy = _____

R + oy = _____

Now use each word to fill in these sentences. The pictures will help you.

This is _____.

Roy has a new _____.

It gives Roy _____.

Roy is a happy _____.

Pair the letter **o** with the letter **y** to create an **oy** sound, like in **boy**. Put the first letter and the letters **oy** together to make new words on the lines below.

b + oy = __boy__

j + oy = __joy__

t + oy = __toy__

R + oy = __Roy__

Now use each word to fill in these sentences. The pictures will help you.

This is __Roy__.

Roy has a new __toy__.

It gives Roy __joy__.

Roy is a happy __boy__.

Questions

Point to the word
in the sentence that
has a soft **C** sound.

There were two clowns at the circus.

Point to the words
in the sentence that
have a hard **G** sound.

The girl was gentle with the old gate.

Pair the letters **oo** together to create an **oo** sound, like in **boot**. Match each picture to the correct **oo** word below.

boot   broom   goose   spoon   tooth

Point to the word in the sentence that has a soft **C** sound.

There were two clowns at the **circus**.

Point to the words in the sentence that have a hard **G** sound.

The **girl** was **gentle** with the old **gate**.

Pair the letters **oo** together to create an **oo** sound, like in **boot**. Match each picture to the correct **oo** word below.

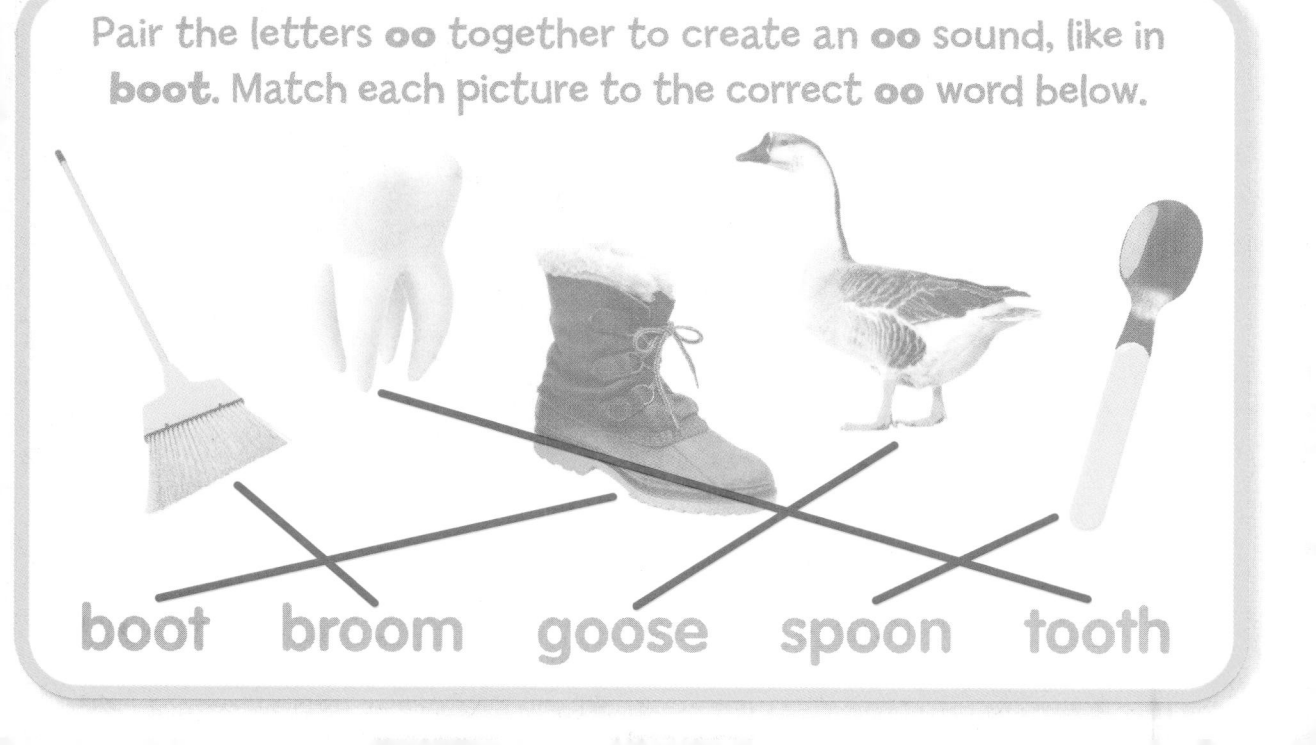

boot   broom   goose   spoon   tooth